MAKING THE ADOBE BRICK

EUGENE H. BOUDREAU

1971
FIFTH STREET PRESS

Copyright © 1971 by Eugene H. Boudreau
All rights reserved

First printing, September 1971
Second printing, October, 1972
Third printing, May 1973

Cover design, Book design by Anne Kent Rush
Photographs by John Pearson
Printed and Bound by Murray Printing
Forge Village, Massachusetts.

Published by Fifth Street Press
1409 Fifth Street
Berkeley, California 94710
Fifth Street Press is an imprint of the Bookworks

Library of Congress Catalog Card Number: 71-178955
ISBN# 0-394-70617-X

Distributed in the United States by Random House, Inc.,
and in Canada by Random House of Canada, Ltd.

CONTENTS

To my beautiful, vivacious and hard-working wife.

The author wishes to thank the following sources for permission
to quote from their material in this book:

Sonoma County Public Health Service for permission to
reprint "Percolation Test Procedure".

Sonoma County Building Inspection Department for permission
to reprint "Fireplace and Chimney Details".

International Conference of Building Officials for permission
to reprint from THE UNIFORM BUILDING CODE
STANDARD NO. 24-15-70

INTRODUCTION

The purpose of this book is to acquaint the reader with all the information necessary to make adobe bricks that conform to the specifications of the Uniform Building Code, and thus can be used for building a home or other structure.

My wife and I made 7,000 adobe bricks, totaling about 120 tons, and then built a nine room house with them. Much of my knowledge was gained through trial and error as I had no previous experience in this art, being a geologist by trade.

Several persons have told me that they once had the intention of making adobe bricks but that the lack of good information on the subject had kept them from ever getting started. If the reader has similar ideas and is similarly frustrated, then perhaps this book will "engage his gears" for him. Good results can be accomplished if the prospective adobe-maker follows the basic ideas herein, uses common sense and is willing to perform a great amount of hard manual labor.

Man has been making adobe bricks for several thousand years, and although they have constituted the main building material in several parts of the world the average American knows little more about them than to ask an experienced adobe-maker, "Do you use any straw?" The knowledge that the Israelites were forced to make them without straw for Pharoah seems an intrinsic part of most people's basic learning. Even though the uncomplicated procedure of making adobes is little known or practiced in the United States, there is a wide and deep regard for the appearance of adobes and of structures built with them, perhaps because they signify "Mother Earth."

"Plain as a mud wall" is an old expression implying a great lack of physical beauty. However, any study of the real estate columns in today's newspapers will show that "adobe" is a prestige word certifying artistic uniqueness and premium quality in a house, and also a higher price. Apart from homes built entirely of adobe, the existence of an adobe fireplace or patio wall receives special mention, and I have even seen a stucco home revered as being "adobe colored".

The fact that adobes do not require any complicated technology in their manufacture and that structures made of them are pleasing to the eye has not generated any great wave of increased use. Partly this is because it is a lot of hard work, and partly because the adobe is not a part of the average American's heritage and thus the necessary knowledge is not diffused throughout his awareness of what is possible. A big obstacle to anyone trying to learn how to make acceptable adobes is the fact that little has been written on the subject, and most of that is out of print. An even larger obstacle is that much of the literature, past and present, that I have read is out of date, does not comply with the specifications of the Uniform Building Code, and contains many omissions of important information, some outright misinformation, and too much over-generalization.

The Uniform Building Code is a set of standards for construction that has been adopted in many areas of the U. S. Any construction with adobe in these areas must conform with the provisions in the Code that deal with adobe. Following the Code means safe and sound construction.

Of course there are many adobe buildings in the world that are not built according to the Code, and every year earthquakes knock down thousands of them. In these buildings, the adobe bricks are not waterproofed, mud is used for mortar, no reinforcing steel is used, and no bond beam is poured along the top of the wall. The traditional method of protecting adobe walls against rain is with wide roof eves and/or a skin of mud plaster, with the plaster requiring periodic patching as it erodes away. It follows that the traditional method of building with adobe is suitable only in arid or semiarid lands where there is no possibility of earthquakes of any great magnitude.

This book began as a work limited to the subject of how to make adobe bricks. Then, the publisher suggested that it would be helpful to include a section on laying adobe bricks, as anyone wanting to make adobes would undoubtedly want to build something with them. This I could do, but the building of adobe walls involves knowing about such things as foundations, electrical outlets, reinforcing steel, bond beams, etc.

The solution was to expand the book to tell something of how my wife and I planned and built our adobe home, which will help the reader by acquainting him with many of the things that enter into any type of adobe construction. Added to this are information sheets in the Appendix and the names of reference sources which I found useful; some of these may be obtained from local libraries or bookstores.

To my knowledge, building with adobe is the only way that a family with no experience and little money can come to own a truely fine home and not be deeply in debt when it's finished. To this can be added the observation that it is a useful, viable, and highly appreciated form of self-expression.

For a family to build an adobe home is a task of monumental proportions. Although I have read that it should always be looked on as "fun," I found that the exigent attitude of "NO EXCUSES! GET MOVING! NOW!" that was imbued in me during my days in the Marine Corps was what got the work done. Then, of course, there was the lure of the Challenge. Further inspiration can be derived from reading such classics as Victor Hugo's *Toilers of the Sea*, and Kipling's poem "If".

MAKING

THE

ADOBE   BRICK

BASIC COMPONENTS

Adobe bricks consist mainly of a mixture of sand and clay to which, in order to conform with the requirements of the Uniform Building Code, a waterproofing substance is added. A good general way to regard the sand and clay in an adobe is to liken them to the components of concrete. In this comparison, the sand in the adobe fills the role of the sand and gravel aggregate in concrete; in other words, it is an inert filler. Clay in the adobe is the binder, as is the cement component in concrete.

Even as the proportion of cement in concrete is less than that of the aggregate, so a proper adobe brick mix usually contains less clay than sand. This is true even though a popular misconception is that adobe bricks must be made of high clay content "adobe" soil. Remember that when "adobe" soil dries out under the summer sun it shrinks up and develops numerous wide and deep cracks, an effect not wanted in adobe bricks.

The Uniform Building Code states that the clay content of adobe bricks must be greater than 25% and less than 45%. Too much clay and the brick develops cracks as it dries; too little clay and the brick will be too weak when it dries and will crumble easily.

• Sand

Not much can be said about this except that a sharp coarse sand is better than fine-grained or rounded types. Sand from ocean beaches cannot be used because its salt content could give bad results.

As my soil had too high a clay content, I had to add sand, which we bought by the truckload from a local building supply company. The cost was $6 per yard, delivered.

• Clay

The term clay refers to an assemblage of mineral particles, most of which are hydrated aluminum silicates, which are of such a small size that they are less than 0.005 millimeters in diameter. This assemblage is plastic when moist and hard when dried. The actual clay minerals are the hydrated aluminum silicates and they are divided into 3 main groups; the kaolin group, the montmorillonite group, and the illite group. These groups differ chemically from each other, and their molecular arrangements, or crystal structures, are also different.

The type of crystal structure is the most important feature in a clay mineral's suitability for making adobes. Kaolin group clays have non-expanding type crystal structures, while clays of the montmorillonite and illite groups have expanding-type crystal structures. Clays with expanding-type crystal structures will hydrate and thus expand considerably in volume in the presence of water, with consequent excessive shrinking and cracking as they lose the excess water upon drying.

From the above it is clear that soils containing a high percentage of kaolin group minerals in the clay fraction are to be preferred for making adobes.

The chief reason for this is that even a high clay content soil can be used without fear of excessive cracking and the result will be stronger bricks. A high clay content of non-kaolin clays means that too much sand must be added, which detracts from the strength of the bricks. Also, kaolin clays are not nearly as sticky as the others and thus are easier to handle.

In the mercury mining district of Sain Alto in the state of Zacatecas, Mexico, I have seen adobes made from high-kaolin clay soil used to make retorts for the distillation of mercury from cinnabar ore and these adobes did not crack or crumble from the 1,000 F. heat. I was told that moisture had little affect on new uncured adobes.

Kaolin clays, because of their desireable characteristics, are widely used in making ceramics, pipe, chinaware and firebricks.

Kaolin clays can be formed by natural weathering of feldspar minerals in granitic rocks or by hydrothermal alteration. The color of pure kaolin is white. Information on the location of deposits of kaolin clays or soils high in such clays should be obtainable from local geologists or geologists with such government offices as the California Division of Mines and Geology. Sonoma County, California, where I live, has several deposits near Nunn Canyon.

The above stress on the desireability of using kaolin clays does not mean that they alone are useable. The soil that I used contained non-kaolin clays. However, if there is a choice, or if kaolin clays are readily available, it would pay you to go to some trouble and expense to get them. Also, some potential adobe-makers may have no soil of their own to use and will have to import it by the truckload to the manufacturing site. Again, a high sand content soil may need the addition of some clay.

• Straw

My experience with using straw in adobes is that it is absolutely necessary in order to prevent a high degree of cracking in the brick, even when the clay content is as low as 30-35%. Straw does not give added strength to adobes but serves to make the brick dry and shrink as one unit. Without it, more than one center of contraction develops and major cracks appear. You have to cut the straw into lengths of about 4 inches or it will all too readily wrap around the blades of the paddles of your mud mixer. Feed stores sell straw by the bale, for about $1.50. If possible, do not use hay.

• Stabilizer

The Uniform Building Code requires that adobes be stabilized to such an extent that if they come in contact with water they will absorb no more than 2.5%, in relation to 100% of their weight. Emulsified asphalt is the required stabilizing agent.

There may be more than one variety of emulsified asphalt, but my experience is limited to a type called RS1, which I bought from a local oil dealer, and from a local road paving company. The cost depends on the quantity purchased, but it cost me about 17 cents per gallon.

Emulsified asphalt consists of tiny droplets of asphalt dispersed in water. RS1 is a brown, sticky liquid which sellers store in heated tanks so that the asphalt will not congeal and settle out. You should not let your RS1 sit around too long because the more congealing and settling the less effective the stabilizer. It helps on cool days to set 5 gallon cans of it over a small fire to heat it to make pouring and mixing with the cool mud easier and quicker. Heating the water used in preparing the mud will also help. On warm days, simply set the RS1 in the sun.

Emulsified asphalt serves to waterproof adobes but it does not contribute to their strength; in fact, superfluous amounts will weaken the brick.

The thought of adding asphalt to an adobe brick may cause the reader to envision something that looks and smells like tar, but this is not the case. I found that the outside color of my adobes turned out to be a natural-enough-looking buff color, and that after a short time the volatiles had evaporated from the asphalt and the adobes smelled only of dry dirt. If the very thought of asphalt is enough to destroy the important esthetic illusions in a person's mind it might be helpful to remember that the ancient inhabitants of Sumer and Babylon mined asphalt from naturally occuring deposits for use as a mortar to hold their adobes together.

Portland cement can be added to soil to give a strong brick which will not be damaged by water. These bricks are not waterproof, as are those properly made with emulsified asphalt, and so do not meet the requirements of the Uniform Building Code. However, because of their greater hardness they would serve well for porch floors and garden walks. Use about 15% cement and keep the bricks damp for a few days so the cement will cure properly.

MOLDS

A mold can be nothing more than 4 boards tacked together with a couple of handles added, but there are refinements which can be incorporated to achieve more uniformly shaped bricks and to prolong the life of the mold.

Use Douglas fir lumber for the mold as it is strong and will hold nails and wood screws much better than pine or redwood. The boards should be of fine-grained, finished lumber as a ribby grain or a rough surface will not separate easily from the mud. Waterproofing the boards is a good idea.

Adobes look best when they come in large sizes. The standard sizes for adobes are: 4X7½X16 inches, used in double courses with a 1 inch mortar joint for the 16 inch wide bearing walls in solid wall construction and also in the curtain walls of post and beam construction, and 4X12X18 inches, used in solid wall construction for non-bearing walls. (see Research and Design, page 00)

The length and width of the desired brick size should be used for the inside dimensions of the mold, but the depth of the mold should probably be 4¼ inches to achieve a 4 inch thick dry adobe as there is usually some slight slumping of the mud when the mold is removed and the brick shrinks somewhat as it dries. If not compensated for in the depth dimension of the mold, that ¼ inch will add up to 4½ inches, equivalent to laying an extra course, in a normal height wall of 18 courses.

The mold will be strengthened if wood screws are used instead of nails to fasten the sides together. Corner braces, sold in hardware stores, give needed rigidity to the mold; I used 2 of them, placed diagonally from each other in opposite corners. These braces should be countersunk

Adobe Brick Mold

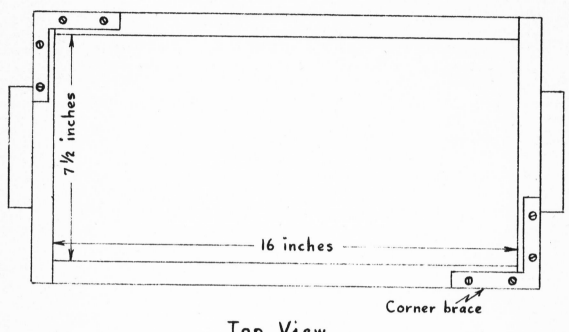

7½ inches

16 inches

Corner brace

Top View

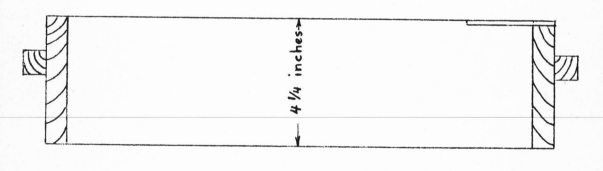

4¼ inches

Side View

so they do not protrude above the rest of the mold.

After the mold has been filled with mud the excess is scraped off with a rectangular mason's trowel, which causes the top of the mold to wear down and become noticeably swaybacked. This wear can be eliminated by tacking a thin strip of metal along the top.

There is often trouble in keeping the mud from clinging to the interior of the mold when it is lifted off; such clinging causes misshaping and corners will pull off the wet brick. A way to facilitate the separation of mud from mold is to line the inside of the mold with thin sheet metal. Another way is to make the bottom of the mold slightly wider than the top, about 1/16 inch on each side.

Double molds can be made but the divider piece should be of 2 inch thick lumber. The reason for the 2 inch divider is that the slumping of the sides of wet adobes will sometimes be as great as ½ inch and thus the adjacent sides of pairs of adobes will touch if only 1 inch lumber is used. Space must be left for air circulation so that drying can take place.

Gravity Separation Soil Test

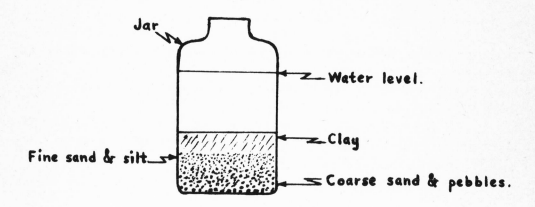

TESTING THE SOIL

A simple way to test a soil for its suitability for making adobe bricks is as follows:

1. With a shovel, remove any sod, leaf mold, or other high organic material from a small part of the area you wish to test.

2. Dig a hole down as deep as you plan to go in your excavating for soil and thoroughly mix what you have taken from the hole. This must be done because soils often have profiles, or horizontal layers, of different composition, and their average is needed.

3. Take a handful of the soil and put it in a jar with some water and shake until the soil turns to mud; then set the jar down and let the solids settle out until the water becomes clear.

4. Examine the settled contents of the jar. Any small pieces of rock in the soil will be at the bottom; next will be the sand, with the coarsest on the bottom and grading upward into silt-size particles; uppermost in the column is the clay, distinguishable by the lack of any visable particles. If some of the clay is rubbed between the fingers it will feel like soap and no gritty particles can be felt.

5. Estimate the % of the column occupied by the clay and the % occupied by the coarser size particles. The Uniform Building Code requires that the amount of clay-size material fall within the range of 25-45%.

Another method of determining the composition of the soil is to have a screen test made by a commercial testing laboratory, which will cost about $5. This will give the % of the total material which will pass through a 200 mesh per inch screen and thus be classifiable as clay size.

After either of the above testing methods have shown that the soil in question does not have more or less clay-size material than the prescribed range, mix some of it into a stiff mud and make several full-size bricks. The reason for making full size bricks for test purposes is that some soils will react very differently in the drying process depending upon the relative amount involved. The first test bricks that I made of my soil were only 2X4X4 inches and showed no cracks when dry, but my first full-size bricks of the same soil resembled jigsaw puzzles when dry.

Dry some of your test bricks in the sun, but dry some of the others in the shade to see which drying conditions they respond to best. Shade can be provided by a piece of plywood set an inch or two above the bricks.

Excessive cracking can be checked by shading, or by adding more sand or straw. If they are going to appear, cracks show up on the first day or two.

If your soil tests out to be too high in either sand or clay content you can obtain sand or high clay soil from a local building materials firm for blending to correct whichever deficiency exists.

When the adobes pass the drying tests it is then time to make some with emulsified asphalt to see how much of the stabilizer will be needed. Before beginning production, it is wise to have some tests made for compressive strength, modulus of rupture, absorption, and moisture content by a commercial laboratory*. It takes several weeks in the sun to get the moisture content of adobes down to the allowed maximum of 4.0%, but this can be hurried by using a warm oven with the door open after the adobes are firm enough to be handled.

*your county building permit office can recommend one.

TESTING THE STABILIZED BRICK

Experiments must be made to determine the amount of emulsified asphalt needed to stabilize adobes made from the soil you have already tested and found suitable for use. This can be done in the following manner:

1. Measure out 1 cubic foot of loose soil by filling a box of 1 cubic foot capacity.

2. Dump this soil into a wheelbarrow and hoe in enough water to make a stiff mud.

3. Slowly add ½ gallon of emulsified asphalt to the mud while mixing thoroughly with your hoe, and continue to mix until the asphalt is no longer discernable. The figure of ½ gallon per cubic foot of soil is the ratio that I've found to be satisfactory.

4. Hand-shape the mud into bricks small enough to be of convenient size, say 2X3X4 inches.

5. Dry the bricks. You can use a warm oven to avoid the long wait necessary when drying in the sun.

6. Take a dry test brick and immerse it in water for several hours. If the brick is sufficiently stabilized, no softening will have occurred, even on the edges. If the test is unsatisfactory then repeat it using more emulsified asphalt. Even if the test is satisfactory it should be repeated with the use of less stabilizer to see if less will give the same good results.

7. After finding out the stabilizer to soil ratio you can figure how much to add per mixer load according to the capacity of your mixer in cubic feet of soil.

It is best to use a little more stabilizer than the minimum found necessary in the testing as conditions may change somewhat while you are in production. I found that even a slight reduction below the minimum resulted in a great lessening in the bricks' resistance to water. And give the stabilizer time enough to mix completely with the mud.

MAKING ADOBES

- Equipment Needed

1. Molds for the various size adobes to be made.

2. A pointed nose shovel for excavating soil and a square point shovel for shoveling mud from flat surfaces.

3. A pick for hard ground.

4. A sturdy, high-sided wheelbarrow with a broad rubber tire.

5. Containers for emulsified asphalt.

6. Trowels for removing excess mud from the molds.

7. A large washtub for washing the molds.

8. Gloves. I used the thin type used by women to protect their hands while dishwashing. They don't last long, but they don't interfere with your movements.

9. Various buckets and a couple of large drums for water storage.

10. A mechanical mud mixer. I bought a used plaster mixer, run by a gasoline engine, which could mix 2 cubic feet of mud at a time. An adequate mixer must have paddles of some sort which stir up the mud and scrape it from the sides. Cement mixers do not serve the purpose. Check with dealers in used machinery, or new if you have the money. The old method of mixing the mud in a pit with the feet will not serve if emulsified asphalt is to be mixed in, for all that it is more "ethnic".

11. Made up casting surfaces and shade providers, which are optional. Adobes can be cast on level ground, but it is more convenient to use such a surface as that provided by plywood or boards. A friend of mine, Andy Johnson, gave me a truckload of long, superannuated foundation forms. These were 20 inches wide, and made of ⅜ inch plywood backed by a framework of 2X4 lumber. They were excellent for

the purpose. I had to use more foundation forms as shade providers because the adobes required shade and because numerous squirrels came to make their homes under the forms on which the adobes were cast and the neighborhood's dogs came to chase the squirrels across the rows of damp adobes.

• Mixing and Casting

Your soil should be mixed and broken up as it is excavated so that the different profiles or layers, if there are more than one, are converted to one essentially homogeneous mass. By wetting down the excavated soil beforehand and covering it with a sheet of plastic the mixing process can be speeded up. A lot of time can be wasted in waiting for stubborn hard lumps of clay to break down into mud.

When measuring your cubic foot of soil for experimenting with the emulsified asphalt you should have noted the number of shovelfuls it took to fill the box. Multiply shovelfuls per cubic foot by the capacity of your mixer in cubic feet and shovel in this amount as you charge the mixer.

When ready to mix mud, first start the mixer and add most of the amount of water that you estimate will be needed. Shovel in the soil and then add just enough more water to make a stiff mud. Sloppy mud is useless. Allow the paddles time enough to beat the mud until all the lumps are gone and then slowly add the required amount of emulsified asphalt and let this mix in for a couple of minutes. The last thing to be added is the straw, and as soon as this is fairly evenly scattered through the mass discharge it from the mixer into a wheelbarrow. Leaving the straw to mix too long will make it tend to separate out by wrapping around the paddles. When the straw is added the mixer may act like it is overloaded; this is because the mass of mud clots together and the paddles encounter a lot more resistance.

Prepare the casting surface by sprinkling it with a little sand or straw to prevent the mud from sticking to it (which could cause cracks), and dunk the mold in a tub of water, again for the purpose of preventing sticking. Put the mold on the casting surface and fill it with mud, pressing it in with the hands and being sure to fill in the corners. Use a trowel to strike the mud level with the top of the mold, and then lift the mold slowly and evenly away from the newly created adobe brick. A properly stiff mud will stand with vertical or only slightly bulged sides when the mold is removed. There is no reason to allow the mud to set for a while in the mold before removing it.

The mold must be cleaned of remnants of clinging mud by dunking in the tub of water before proceeding to make the next adobe.

Drying & Curing of Adobes
Side View

Weight to prevent wind from dislodging cover

Drying adobes

Shade cover

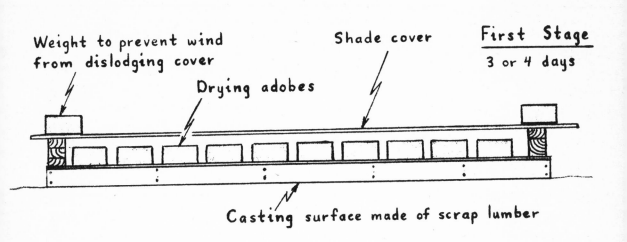

Casting surface made of scrap lumber

Cover removed & adobes stood up on one side when they are firm

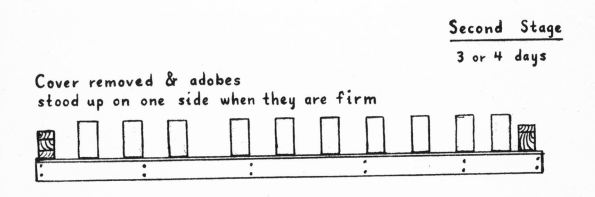

Remove from casting surface & allow to dry in well-spaced rows.

• Drying and Curing

If newly made adobes do not have a chance to dry evenly they will tend to slump and crack, since wet mud is not very stable. Cold foggy weather is bad, and they must be protected from rain as well during the first 3 or 4 days. Protection should be provided above the adobes but not on the sides as the wind will help them dry. Once I covered a row of adobes, top and sides, with a sheet of plastic to shield them from a spring shower and I found the next day that they had all developed cracks and slumped sides because the plastic had kept all moisture from escaping. Another time, I lost a day's production because I tried shading them with roofing felt laid directly on top of the new adobes and overlapping onto the ground; the result was the same as with the plastic. Shade and protect, but don't stifle.

Your bricks may dry perfectly under such ideal weather as mild spring days, but a spell of hot, dry, windy days may cause widespread cracking in new bricks no matter what you do. Burlap sacks can be hung over the edges of the shade providers to protect the bricks from dry winds.

When bricks crack in the drying process it is often directly in the center, but that is no loss as many partial bricks are needed in building.

Once I decided to groove the tops of some of my new bricks in order that the mortar would have a better bond when they were laid up in a wall. The next day, I found that those surface grooves had turned to cracks which extended clear through the bricks.

As soon as your bricks have dried for 3 or 4 days you should then stand them up on one side so that the drying will be more rapid and even. Shade providers probably won't be needed beyond this point. About 6 weeks of drying in the sun is long enough to get the moisture content down to the required maximum of 4.0%, and then the bricks can be stacked in rows several high to get them out of the way. Stack the bricks where they won't interfere with future construction or traffic.

Molds not in use can be kept in a barrel of water to prevent them from drying out and beginning to part at the joints, or warp.

Personal experience with daily rates of adobe production showed that I could make a maximum of about 70 of the 4X7½X16 inch adobes, or 35 of the 4X12X18 inch adobes in 8 or 9 hours of continuous hard work. Often I could not achieve this level of production because there were bricks to be stacked, dirt to be excavated, etc. My maximum level of production added up to about one ton of adobes per man per day, and this weight had to be handled several times in the process of turning undisturbed soil into a stack of cured bricks.

Discharging mud from the plaster mixer. Its gasoline engine is enclosed. This machine sits by your excavation site.

Filling the mold. Note the inside of this mold is lined with tin. The casting surface is made from scrap plywood supported by 2x4's.

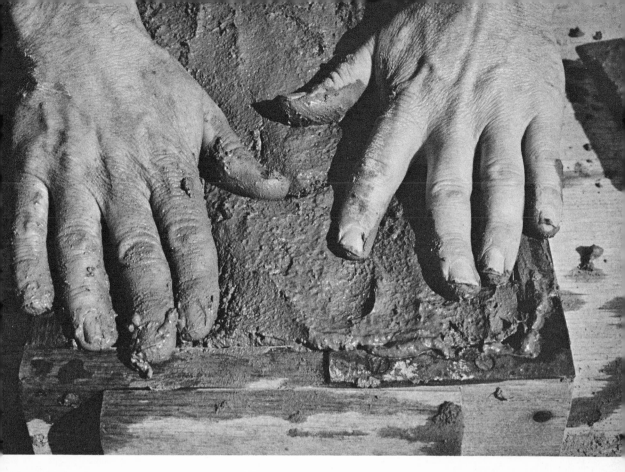

Working the mud into the corners of the mold. You can see the iron corner brace screwed to the mold.

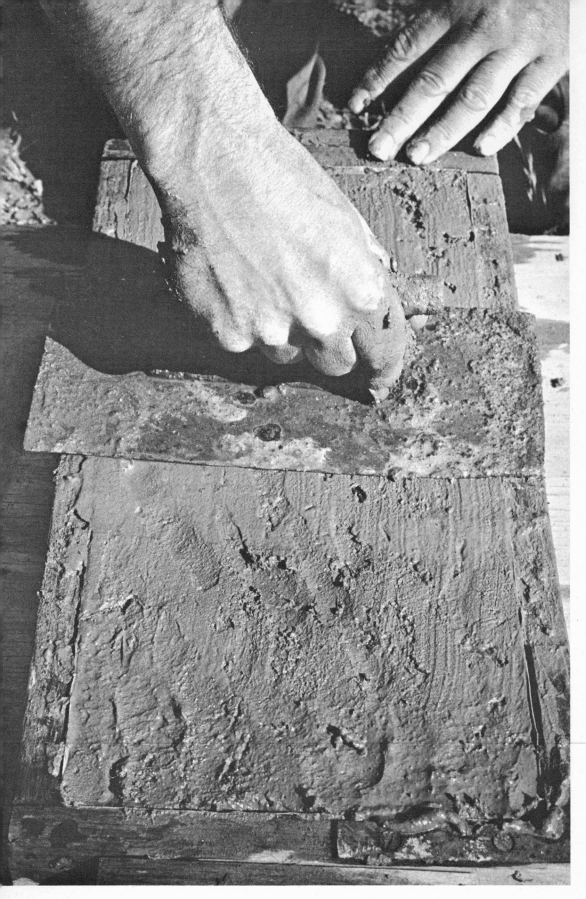

Using a trowel to strike the mud level with the top of the mold.

Lifting the mold slowly and evenly to avoid pulling off a corner. If you mixed a good stiff mud, the unsupported wet brick will not sag more than one-quarter inch.

Washing the mold. If you don't, the corners of the next brick will tear off on mud left from the last one.

Drying bricks where they lay cast, for the first three or four days.

Adding a shade cover.

Drying bricks on edge.

BUILDING

WITH

ADOBE BRICK

RESEARCH & DESIGN

In 1965, I was very much committed to the idea of becoming a home-owner. We had 2 children, we were fed up with living in rented apartments, and we liked the Santa Rosa area where we were living in California. Surely, we wanted a good size lot for privacy and play room for the children, an ample floor plan, a distinctive and satisfying design, and good quality construction. We wanted to own such a home while we were still young and we didn't want to acquire a crushing life-long debt in the process.

Somehow, these expansive and expensive tastes had to be reconciled with the not inconsiderable problems of:

1. We didn't own any land.
2. There was little more than $1,000 in our cash resources.
3. Except for some experience in shovel work and mechanical drawing, I had no background in any of the phases of home design or construction.

The situation of such lofty dreams being opposed by such bleak and stubborn realities is common enough, and the dreams usually give way to the grudging acceptance of assuming a 30-year mortgage on a piece of flimsy construction embellished with pseudo-quality veneer. I disdained the idea of contributing years and years of my income in exchange for something materially and esthetically unsatisfactory. It seemed a cruel waste of money and, more important, life.

Somehow, we were going to have to build it with our own hands. "Foreward, the Light Brigade!"

In my mind, the quality construction was to be of some sort of masonry, but all of the details were extremely vague. The catalyst for my thoughts came to my attention in the Santa Rosa Public Library, (originally a gift of Andrew Carnegie) as I was standing in front of the shelves of books on home construction and I saw one about how to build an adobe home. From that moment on I knew what I was going to do, and my first step was to check the book out and begin to read.

I didn't know it at the time, but this old handbook on adobe construction followed standards which were not up to those set by the Uniform Building Code, and it was several months before I even knew that there was such a thing as the U.B.C. After going through several references on adobe I decided to go to the County Building Inspection Department to see just what regulations they had about the subject; there, I was told that the county would approve my house plans if I could get an engineer or architect to approve them.

Not having any plans, I submitted a sketch of the floor plan that I had in mind to an architect and asked him what he would charge to draw up a set. He said that he would charge me a minimum of $1,800 for drawing up the plans and watching over the construction, and that he would have to consult with other architects and engineers on various details, which would add to the cost. My reaction was to decide to make a downpayment on a building site and to begin the task of making adobes; in the evenings and during the winter months I could continue gathering information with the objective of making my own plans.

Shortly afterward, one day in the late spring, we selected a site consisting of an acre and a half of decrepit old apple and pear trees. The nearby homes were of good quality, the ground water was potable, and the site was level enough to simplify foundation design, yet with enough slope to provide good drainage. As a geologist, I could see that it was about as safe an area as possible for minimizing the danger of earthquake damage, for it was not on or adjacent to an active fault, and the ground was weathered rock in place and not unconsolidated alluvium.

Unconsolidated alluvium is recent sediment deposited in valleys, lakes or bays by streams, and as it has never been buried very deeply it still has some settling to do if a load is put on it. This tendency to settle causes problems in foundation design, and so such areas should be avoided by heavy structures. Also, in areas subject to earthquakes alluvium tends to magnify the vibrations caused by earthquakes, which increases the probability of damage to structures built on it.

The grass was green, the lupines were in bloom, the sun was warm, and it was time to get started making adobes.

Usable information on planning and construction detail came from many sources:

    1. The University of California at Berkeley sells sets of plans for adobe homes for very cheap prices. Write to:

Agricultural Publications
207 University Hall
University of California
Berkeley, California 94720

2. Hans Sumph Co., which makes adobe bricks, has construction information and diagrams available for no charge. The address is:

    40101 Avenue 10
    Fresno, California 93726

3. Wilson, J. Douglas, *Practical House Carpentry*, McGraw-Hill, 1957.
4. County building inspectors—a very good source.
5. The Uniform Building, Electrical, and Plumbing Codes.
6. Richter, H.P., "Wiring Simplified", Park Publishing, Inc.
7. Building supply companies.
8. Friends who are building contractors or who work in the building trades.
9. Owners of adobe homes.

The floor plan that I finally worked out was for an L-shaped house with a living wing and a sleeping wing. The L was positioned so that the patio and the porch were shielded from the prevailing southwest wind and given a sunny southeast exposure.

There are several methods of approved adobe construction, but the one appealing to my taste was that called "16 inch solid bearing wall". This is more traditional looking than the more popular "post and beam" construction with 7½ inch walls, and it looked to me like it required less engineering. A bearing wall is one which supports any weight other than its own, and any adobe bearing wall must be at least 16 inches thick. Height of adobe bearing walls can be a maximum of 10 times the thickness. Adobe homes can be no more than one story high. No opening in an adobe bearing wall can be over 4 feet wide and keep openings at least 3 feet from corners. Consult the Uniform Building Code for details.

The information available from Hans Sumph Co. covers "steel frame" adobe construction, which uses a hidden framework of steel pipe to take all of the structural stress and strain. "Post and beam" construction uses an exposed framework of 7½ inch timbers that serves the same purpose as the steel pipe; the adobes merely fill in between the timbers.

When I considered what I wanted, I chose to design toward the end of having a home with which I would be completely satisfied when we were finished. The floorplan included 3 bedrooms, 2 baths, an office, a

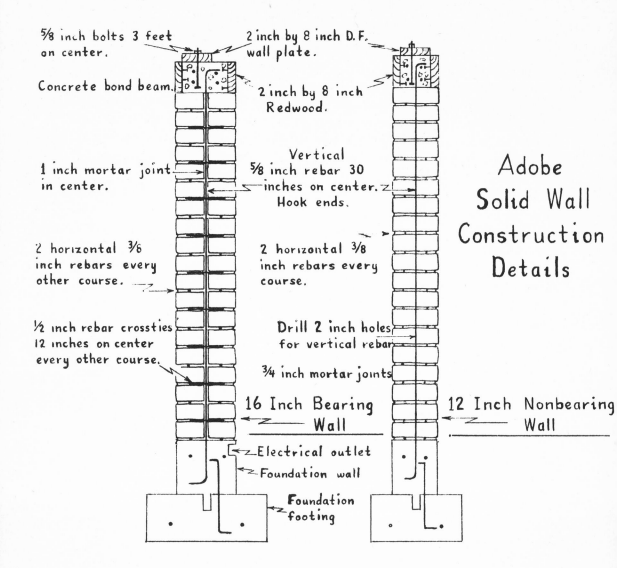

Adobe Solid Wall Construction Details

5/8 inch bolts 3 feet on center.

2 inch by 8 inch D. F. wall plate.

Concrete bond beam.

2 inch by 8 inch Redwood.

1 inch mortar joint in center.

Vertical 5/8 inch rebar 30 inches on center. Hook ends.

2 horizontal 3/8 inch rebars every other course.

2 horizontal 3/8 inch rebars every course.

1/2 inch rebar crossties 12 inches on center every other course.

Drill 2 inch holes for vertical rebar

3/4 inch mortar joints

16 Inch Bearing Wall

12 Inch Nonbearing Wall

Electrical outlet

Foundation wall

Foundation footing

big combined living room and dining room, a kitchen, and a service room. The porch was a hearty 60 feet long and 7 feet wide. Useable floor space, exclusive of the porch and areas occupied by walls, amounts to about 1450 square feet. Each room was considered on the basis of what it would be used for and given correspondingly adequate dimensions. Four by four inch porch posts would have served to support the porch roof, but 8 X 8 inch posts were more in character with the massive aspect of the rest of the house. 3/8 inch plywood sheeting on the roof was good enough for structural strength, but I added 2 X 8 inch T & G pine for visual effect with the exposed beam framing members, and for insulation. Aluminum window frames are cheap and easy to install, but they look out of place in an adobe home so I bought lumber, screws and glue and made my own swing-out double casement windows.

To make them is not difficult. Buy sash stock at a sash and door shop, cut the pieces at a 45° angle in a miter box, and put them together

with exterior wood glue and a couple of long wood screws at each joint.
Use clamps to hold them together until the glue dries. Allow an eighth
of an inch clearance all the way around to avoid problems with swelling
in wet weather. 1 inch by 8 inch V-Rustic pine was used to cover the
gable ends and the 4 wood partition walls in the home. All this kept us
broke, but now there are no regrets.

Making the adobes took our spare time for 2 years during the
months of late spring, summer, and early fall, and when that was
finished the required tests were made (the commercial testing laboratory in San Francisco that did the work told me when I called for
the results that all the test bricks had failed the test for modulus of
rupture, but it turned out that they had misplaced a decimal point!)

Adobes are made commercially in some places with machinery
capable of producing several thousand per day. To purchase the number of adobes that we made would have cost us about $3,000.

Shortly after winding up our adobe-making I took my nearly completed house plans to an engineer to get his analysis of their structural
competence and so he could recommend proper beam sizes and spacing,
the amount of reinforcing steel needed, the types of beam fasteners, and

Lintel over a casement window, seen from the inside looking out. Note concrete
window sill.

bolt data. The formula followed for figuring the proper amount of reinforcing steel to put in our adobe walls was: "a minimum of 0.002 of the gross cross-sectional area, not more than 2/3 of which may be in either direction." The bill for the engineering calculations, which are in the Appendix of this book, came to $110, which I was quite happy about!

In drawing the plans, I followed the same drafting system as used in some plans that I bought from the University of California. The plans were drawn on 24 X 36 inch tracing paper so blueprint copies could be made easily and cheaply. I used the 1 to 30 scale on my engineer's ruler and counted each division as one inch.

Upon approval by the Sonoma County Building Permit Office of these plans, the work of building the house began. By this time, we had finished paying for the land and could apply our money toward buying construction materials.

THE FOUNDATION

Foundations for adobe buildings are more massive than those of wooden houses as there is more weight to support. Depth of the foundation is dependent on soil conditions and an engineer should be consulted on the matter. Foundation footings must extend beyond the foundation wall on each side by 50% of the width of the wall.

Adobe house builders in Mexico construct foundations by first digging a shallow trench and then laying large rocks in it. The rock work is carried up to about 10 inches above the surface of the ground and then the laying of the adobe bricks begins. By keeping the base of the adobe brick section of the wall well above ground level the undermining effect of splashing rainwater that drips from the eaves is avoided.

As our building site was fairly level and the ground was solid, there were no particular problems in foundation design. Such a book as *Practical House Carpentry* does a good job of instructing you in how to lay out and build foundation forms.

Our foundation trenches were dug with pick and shovel in the heat of the summer, resulting in our moving about 80 tons of dirt and wearing off one inch of blade on my favorite shovel (some 400 tons of dirt had been moved by pick and shovel by the time all phases of construction were finished). To save on lumber, I made the trenches the exact width of the foundation footing; to mark the top of the footing, nails were stuck into the side of the trench.

Two ⅝ rebars were positioned in the trench atop pieces of brick and then ready-mix concrete was poured in. If a fireplace is wanted, a 12 inch deep reinforced concrete pad for it must be poured, with the rebar tied into the foundation.

It took about 3 months from the time that I started digging the foundation trenches to the time the last of the concrete was poured. Ready-mix concrete, which is brought to the site in concrete-mixer trucks, costs about $20 per cubic yard. You can't mix your own that cheap. As the pouring of the foundation footing was finished, pieces of 2 X 4 inch lumber were set in the fresh concrete and then removed when the concrete was firm. This provided a key to later help bond the foundation wall to the foundation footing. To further anchor the two together, 2 foot long pieces of $\frac{5}{8}$ rebar were stuck into the fresh concrete at 30 inch intervals. See my diagram of Adobe Solid Wall Construction for details.

Next, forms for the foundation wall were set up and more readymix was poured. To provide for the vertical $\frac{5}{8}$ inch rebar needed for the adobe wall, I used a measuring tape and pieces of 1 X 2 inch lumber with holes in them to position the rebars and hold them in place while pouring. Electrical outlet boxes and connecting conduit were wired to the insides of the forms where necessary, it being more difficult to cut outlets in adobe walls. Be careful to plug all outlet box screw holes with something to keep the concrete out.

LAYING ADOBE BRICKS

The following equipment is needed for laying adobe bricks up into adobe walls:
1. A 6 foot mason's level for use in keeping the walls vertical.
2. A 2 foot level for leveling individual adobes as they are laid.
3. A ball of nylon string for use as guides to keep the walls level and vertical.
4. A wheelbarrow and a hoe for mixing mortar.
5. A combination rebar cutter and bender.
6. Gloves, thin, for freedom of movement.
7. A brace and bits, or an electric drill with a masonry bit, for drilling holes in adobes.
8. Wire brush for cleaning rebar.
9. Shovel.
10. Various buckets.
11. Brick Splitter.

The first step is to clean the top of the foundation and lay 2 parallel ⅜ inch rebars about 3 inches in from the edges. Rebar should be free of material such as dirt, loose rust scale, oil, etc. to ensure a good bond with the mortar.

The next step is to mix up a batch of mortar in your wheelbarrow. Mortar is mixed in the proportion of 1 part Portland Cement to 2½ parts clean sharp sand. As the mortar is required to be waterproof, emulsified asphalt must be added to the mixture in the proportion of 1½ gallons per sack of cement used. Start by shoveling in the amount of sand and cement wanted and mixing it in the dry state. Add clean water, a little at a time, and mix with a hoe until a stiff but moist mixture is obtained (sloppy mortar will squeeze out from under the

50 adobes and will not stay in the vertical joints). When the mortar is the right consistancy, slowly add the emulsified asphalt and mix thoroughly. Use hot water on cold days for less trouble with the asphalt and to keep the hands feeling comfortably warm. Do not use lime in the mortar.

Mortar sets up fast, and I found it best to mix up only a small amount at one time (5 shovelfuls of sand and 2 of cement). If delays cause your mortar to begin to stiffen before it can be used, it is permissable to add a small amount of water and mix to restore the right consistency.

The 120 tons of adobes in the walls of our home required about 30 tons of mortar.

Lay corner bricks first, but before doing so hammer in the nails needed to anchor your string guides. It is easier to lay either the outside or the inside course of a 16 inch wall at one time, but not both together as shifting mortar causes trouble. Wet the top of the foundation and place some mortar on it. Spread the mortar out with your gloved hands (I bought some expensive pointed mason's trowels, but never used them) until it looks fairly level and about ¾ inch thick. Clean the bottom of an adobe of loose dirt, wet it, set it on the mortar and slide it back and forth a little so that the bottom is completely in contact with mortar. Use your small level to see that the tops of the corner adobes are level both lengthwise and crosswise, and also use it to be sure that the outboard sides are in the same vertical plane as the sides of the foundation. If adjustments are needed, use sliding motions or taps with your fist to move the adobe and then recheck with the level.

After the corner bricks have set long enough for the mortar to dry, it is time to place the string guides which help in laying the rest of the bricks in the course. Tie a nylon string to the base of the nail in the top of one corner brick and then pull it tight and tie it to the base

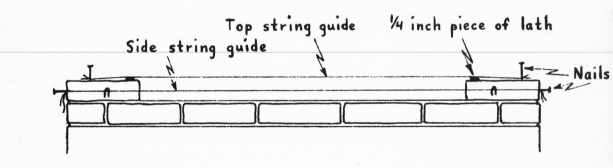

Setting String Guides for Laying Adobes

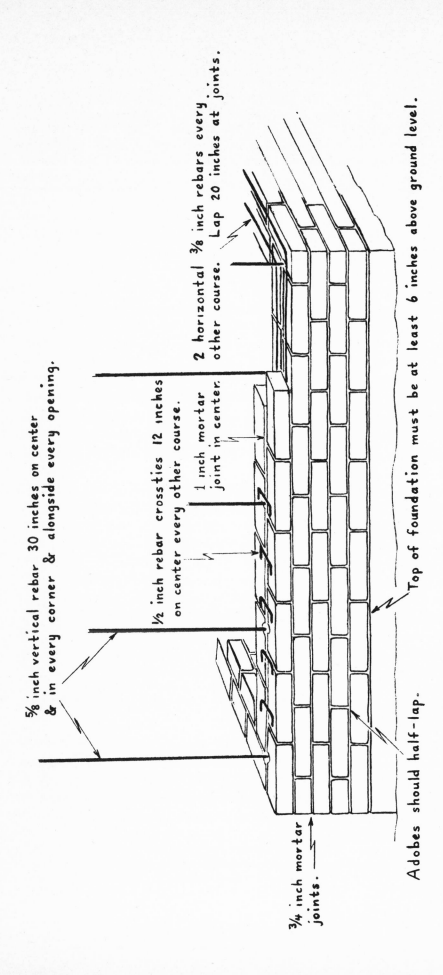

5/8 inch vertical rebar 30 inches on center & in every corner & alongside every opening.

1/2 inch rebar crossties 12 inches on center every other course.

2 horizontal 3/8 inch rebars every other course. Lap 20 inches at joints.

1 inch mortar joint in center.

3/4 inch mortar joints.

Adobes should half-lap.

Top of foundation must be at least 6 inches above ground level.

Adobe Construction Details
16 Inch Solid Wall

of the nail in the top of another corner brick; do the same with a string for the nails in the sides of the bricks. Place a piece of lath under the string in front of both top string guide nails to raise the string about ¼ inch; hook a couple of bent nails or staples over the side string guide to hold it out from the sides of the corner bricks about ⅛ inch. These string guides now allow the laying of the adobes between the corner bricks without anymore recourse to the level except to use it to level the tops of the adobes in the crosswise direction. By eye, keep the adobes away from the string guides by the amount of clearance set with the pieces of lath and bent nails at the corner bricks. I used individual string guides for up to 50 foot long stretches of wall, but I divided the 80 foot back wall into 40 foot sections to avoid complications from sagging of the top string and wind movement of the side string.

As the wall gets higher, use the 6 foot level to keep the corner bricks vertical with the side of the foundation.

Lay adobes from the corners toward the centers of the walls, and overlap them by 50% as much as possible. Fill the vertical joints with mortar after completing a course. If you wish the adobes to project in relief, then you can rake the mortar joints back a half inch with your fingers before the mortar hardens.

If a space needs a less than full-size adobe you can make one with your brick splitter and hammer. First, groove the adobe all the way around with a nail, and then place the splitter at various places along the groove and tap it with the hammer, hitting progressively harder until the adobe splits along the groove. Adobes are homogeneous in structure with no preferred cleavage planes, and so the tapping creates a plane of weakness.

Where door or window openings are to occur, set vertical nailing block frames of 2 X 4 inch Douglas Fir. These are for the purpose of fastening door and window frames. The nailing blocks are recessed into the wall by notching the ends of the adobes, and they are fastened to the wall by driving a couple of 16 penny nails into the blocks at the level of each horizontal joint and letting the nails protrude into the joint space so they will be held by the mortar.

The non-bearing adobe partition walls in the home are made of the 4 X 12 X 18 inch adobes and are 12 inches wide. Holes must be drilled in the adobes where the vertical rebars do not correspond with vertical joints. An electric drill with a masonry bit would be the easy way to drill these holes, but I used a brace with a ¾ inch wood bit. These wood bits lasted for about 7 holes and then they were shot. Holes were enlarged to a diameter of 2 inches with a rasp.

The rate at which I laid adobes was a maximum of 60 per day of

Nailing Blocks

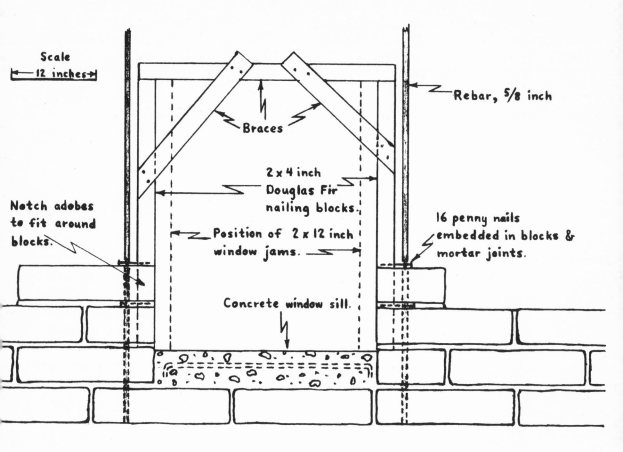

Scale
|← 12 inches →|

Rebar, 5/8 inch

Braces

2 x 4 inch
Douglas Fir
nailing blocks.

Notch adobes
to fit around
blocks.

Position of 2 x 12 inch
window jams. →

16 penny nails
embedded in blocks &
mortar joints.

Concrete window sill.

the 4 X 7½ X 16, and 25 per day of the 4 X 12 X 18 inchers. I was slow
and careful, and the results were good.

Two electric light switch boxes had to be placed in the adobe walls.
This was done by putting in the boxes and laying adobes around them.
A piece of conduit extended from each box to the center mortar joint
in the wall and then upward to just above the top of where the bond
beam was to be.

My scaffolding for working on the walls consisted of 55 gallon
drums and planks.

LINTELS, BOND BEAM, AND WALL PLATE

"A Lintel is a horizontal architectural member spaning and usually carrying the load above an opening," according to Webster's Dictionary. Lintels in old adobe homes were often made of wood, but now they must be of reinforced concrete extending at least 20 inches beyond each side of the opening. For details, see the engineering calculations in the Appendix.

I used 2 X 8 inch Redwood for the sides of the lintel forms, and after the concrete set, these were left in place. The bottoms of the forms over the openings were of ⅝ inch plywood, CDX, held in place with clamps. So that the wood would remain fastened to the concrete, I drove nails through the plywood into the interior of the forms, and from the inside of the forms I drove nails part way into the Redwood.

A bond beam is a continuous layer of concrete which is poured along the top of the adobe wall, thus tying together the vertical ⅝ inch rebars which come up through the adobe walls from the foundation. Forms here were constructed in the same manner as for the lintels. Before pouring the concrete for the bond beam I had to position the bolts for the fastening of the wall plate and the angle irons that would be holding the rafters and joists of the roof, which was done with strips of plywood with holes drilled in them. Again, see the Appendix for details.

Concrete for lintels and bond beam was mixed by hand, using 1 part cement to 5 parts aggregate mix. Buckets were used to hoist up about 15 tons of concrete to the top of the wall. The sand and gravel aggregate mix came from a building materials supply company. Pieces of 2 X 10 inch Douglas Fir were bolted to the bond beam for the wall plate. See my engineer's calculations in the Appendix for details.

THE ROOF

The first step in constructing the roof was to buy in advance the Douglas Fir beams needed for the rafters, joists, ridge beam, and porch posts and headers. These I wanted in the rough, and they had to be cut especially at a mill. When they were delivered, we spent 2 days stacking, spacing and shading them so they would dry without warping and cracking. Some warped and cracked anyway.

All of the angle iron and washers for the roof fasteners had to be made up in a machine shop. For clearance, the bolt holes in the angle irons were made 9/16 inch in diameter.

I had thought of hiring a carpenter to help with the framing of the roof, but when the time came to begin there was no money.

When the wall plate and the angle irons had been bolted down, I began the task of getting the beams up onto the top of the wall. This took several days. To get the long heavy joists to the top of the wall I would set them on the top of a 55 gallon drum placed near an outside corner of the wall and then raise one end by pushing down on the other end. When the high end of the beam was higher than the top of the wall I would then pivot it on the drum and swing it over and down to the top edge of the wall. Now, I could heave on the lower end of the beam until it went up and over to fall across the interior angle of the corner.

Spacing of the 4 X 6 inch rafters and joists was set 4 feet on center, except in the living room and the dining room where the joists were 6 X 8 inch beams and set 8 feet on center. First to be set in position and drilled were the joists. Next, pieces of 4 X 4 inch lumber were set on some of the joists along the center line of the roof and the ridge beam was set on these and nailed and braced temporarily.

To set the rafters, I first cut the ridge beam end of a rafter to the

Wall and roof construction. Note lintels over windows on the left, door opening on the right and concrete bond beam running around the wall, capping both. Wall plate sits on the bond beam and anchors ceiling joists and rafters to the wall.

required angle, using a carpenter's square to first measure the angle. This was then butted up against the ridge beam and held in place with a small nail while I held an angle iron fastener in place to mark the positions of the bolt holes; also marked was the position of the seat cut where the rafter was to rest on the wall plate. Holes were drilled slightly oversize, and rafters were made long enough to provide for eaves.

Sections of ridge beam can be spliced together by making 45° angle cuts on the adjoining ends and then nailing them together. Then, lap the splices with 2 three foot long splints of 2 X 8 inch Douglas Fir and fasten these to the beam with 2 ⅝ inch bolts on each side of the splice. Plan the splices so they occur at the midpoints between pairs of rafters.

The valley rafters, which occur where the 2 wings of the roof meet, presented some difficult cuts, but *Practical House Carpentry* taught me how to make them.

The rafters at the gable ends of the roof were supported by 2 X 4 inch studs, 16 inches on center, nailed to the rafters and to the wall plate.

To cover the roof, 2 X 8 inch T & G pine was used. I started laying this at the ridge beam and worked it on down to the eaves, nailing

with two 16 penny nails at each bearing point on a rafter, and staggering
the joints. It was sometimes difficult to get the T & G to fit tightly together, and so I would have to nail a block of wood to the board that
was already nailed down and use a clamp, one hook on the ridge beam
side of the block and one hook on the lower edge of the loose board, to
draw them together.

For structural strength, ⅜ inch plywood was nailed over the T & G.
I used the type called CDX, which is made with exterior type glue so
the weather won't hurt it. Joints were staggered 50%.

Roof beams were all stained before the sheeting was put on, and
the T & G was stained before it was put in place.

Positioning of holes for vent pipes should be done with a plumb bob,
as I found that dropping a rock, which I tried first, is not very accurate.

Porch posts were spaced 12 feet on center to provide plenty of room
for slinging hammocks.

The final covering on the roof was Redwood shakes, nailed to 1 X 4
inch Douglas Fir nailing strips. In the Uniform Building Code there is
a section on specifications for shake and shingle roofs.

PLUMBING

There are no great mysteries or hard-to-acquire skills associated with the installation of a plumbing system in a home. Except for one day of my father's time, I was able to do all of my own plumbing; everything works.

The best way to find out what to do is to study the Uniform Plumbing Code and your local county building ordinances. Information on how to do it can come from asking questions of the building supply people from whom the materials are bought, and I got some help from a well-illustrated do-it-yourself plumbing book (which was not up to Code) from Sears Roebuck. When in doubt, ask your building inspector.

Our water supply is from a well. From the well, a trench was dug 250 feet to the house and plastic pipe, called PVC, was laid in it alongside the wires needed to supply electricity to the pump. PVC is cheaper than metal pipe and will not corrode. It can be cut with a hacksaw, and it is put together with a special glue and slip-on fittings. As the distance from well to house was so great, 1½ inch pipe was used to avoid a pressure drop. A couple of inches of sand were put under the pipe to minimize the chance of differential settling causing the pipe to break when the trench was filled in.

About 2 feet outside the house a tee went on the line to provide branch lines to outside hose bibs for the garden. Then, an adapter went on the line so I could change over to ¾ inch copper pipe. Before entering the house, a gate shut-off valve was put on the line so that the house water could be shut off in case of possible plumbing disasters.

All of the water supply lines in the house are copper. There are different types of copper pipe, determined by the thickness of the wall of the pipe, to be used in different circumstances. The book from Sears gave good instructions on how to solder the pipe and the fittings together, and the only trouble that I had was that at first I would get the fittings too hot and the solder would not adhere to the copper, and once copper has been overheated it will never be solderable. The Sears' book lists the materials and the tools needed to install the various types of plumbing available.

The main ¾ inch cold water pipe has ½ inch branch lines to the kitchen, service room and bathroom fixtures. The various sinks, washbasins and toilets are connected to the ½ inch branch lines by means of ⅜ inch flexible copper tubing. This tubing may be bent with a regular tubing bender or, by filling it with dry sand, by bending it by hand. Shutoff valves connect the pipe and the tubing.

Copper pipe should never come in contact with other metals as electrolysis will destroy the pipe.

At the hot water heater, a check valve and a shut-off valve were installed on the incoming cold water line. A water pressure relief valve was installed on the hot water line outlet and its drain was extended to outside the house. Flexible tubing with attached fittings was used to connect the heater to the water pipes. Hot water lines are ½ inch copper pipe.

Hot and cold water lines for the washing machine have hose bibs on the ends.

To learn about installing toilets I asked questions of the owner of the store where I bought them. The process is simple:

1. Slip toilet ring over end of toilet bend.

2. Caulk lower portion of gap between inside of toilet ring and outside of toilet bend with tow.

3. Fill remainder of gap with molten lead.

4. Press a wax gasket around the toilet bowl outlet.

5. Bolt toilet to toilet ring, tightening the nuts only finger tight to avoid cracking the bowl.

Drain lines are of hubless cast-iron pipe held together with flexible plastic sleeves and stainless steel clamps. The main drain is 4 inch pipe and the feeder drains are 2 inch. The minimum allowable grade is ¼ inch per foot. A rented chain-type pipe cutter was used to cut the pipe.

Vent pipes are used to get rid of gas that forms in the drain lines. They may be of hubless cast-iron pipe, although I used galvanized pipe.

Here is a check list of some of the things to be remembered:

1. House drain must be 3 inches minimum for 2 toilets.

2. All horizontal drain lines require cleanouts, which must be accessable and have 18 inches minimum clearance in front.

3. Use "Combination Y" and "⅛" bends at intersections of hori-

zontal and vertical drain lines.

    4. Keep traps as close to fixtures as possible.

    5. Install sanitary tees at fixture inlets to drain lines.

    6. Approved type of pan or shower intercepter subdrain and 2 inch trap required for shower.

    7. Main vent same size as house drain.

    8. Maximum distance from fixture trap to vent is 24 inches.

    9. Intersections of vertical fixture vents and horizontal vent lines must be at least 6 inches above rim of fixtures served.

    10. Galvanized iron pipe 6 inches minimum clearance above ground or concrete slab floor.

    11. Consult county plumbing ordinance for maximum number of fixtures on each drain or vent line.

    No sewer lines exist in our area, and so a septic tank system had to be installed to treat and dispose of the sewage from the main house drain. Information on how to lay-out this system and make the necessary percolation test was obtained from the county health department (see Appendix for details). We did all of the shovel work ourselves, some 140 tons of dirt moving. A ready-made concrete septic tank and distribution boxes were bought from a dealer, who brought the tank out on a truck with a boom and lowered it directly into the hole with no trouble. I had considered making my own tank, but the time and money involved favored buying one. The 40 yards of drain rock needed, costing $3 per yard, delivered, came from a nearby quarry. See the diagram in the Appendix for lay-outs of typical septic tank systems.

    I was intrigued to learn from some of my reading on Mesopotamian archaeology that 4,000 years ago those people used vertical leach lines for disposal of sewage. These consisted of shafts sunk down for several tens of feet in which were placed strings of perforated fired clay pipe. Broken pottery was filled in around the pipe to act as drain rock.

ELECTRIC WIRING

Wiring a home is more involved than doing the plumbing, but all of the elements are basically simple. By studying the book *Wiring Simplified*, which follows the National Electrical Code, I learned all that I had to know about laying-out circuits and wiring switches and outlets. Another book that helped, and one that has many good illustrations, is the Sears Roebuck book *Simplified Electric Wiring Handbook*, although it does not follow the Code in all respects. The Sears book has an illustrated list of the tools needed and describes their uses. When in doubt, consult your building inspector.

To start my electrical system, I began by studying the above books and laying-out a wiring diagram on a floor plan of the house. The positions of switches and outlets were selected and then they were divided into various circuits. Special circuits for the stove, dryer, and the washing machine were drawn in. I learned about the types of wiring and the conditions under which they may be used. There are tables which describe the sizes of wire which must be used, and the capacities of conduit, switch boxes and outlet boxes for numbers of wires according to size. The information began to seep in.

Conduit embedded in the concrete foundation was used to bring wires to the base outlets in the sections of adobe wall. Romex was used in the wooden partition walls and along the tops of the adobe walls and joist beams. Romex does not have to be concealed if it is more than 8 feet above floor level.

The only tools needed beyond my carpenter's tools were a conduit bender and a tool for cutting and stripping wire.

The actual wiring involved only about 4 different hook-ups. It took time to become familiar with them, but I did them all correctly. Twiston solderless connectors make the connection of wires a simple thing. Clip-on wire clamps ground the ground wires to the switch and outlet boxes. Circuit breakers were used in place of fuses in the main panel.

When it came time to check my circuits, I taped the ends of each circuit together at the main panel and then used a friend's ampmeter to check continuity by making contact at the contact screws of each outlet.

It wasn't until all of the wiring was completed that the power company brought in power to the house. Not wanting power and telephone lines visible around the house, I dug a 220 foot long trench to the nearest power pole and had that section laid underground.

LOOSE ENDS

Probably the most important asset that a prospective adobe home builder can have is the ability to read and understand. That, and the conviction that there is always a way to accomplish things, are much more important than previous experience in any of the building trades. In all phases of planning and building it is necessary to find out and to understand what your county building inspector requires; to consider the types and the merits of materials that can be used; and to find out about and use the proper tools.

Our home cost us about $10,000 to build, exclusive of land and water supply costs. I would estimate that a rectangular-shaped 2 bed-room home with about 1,000 square feet of useable floorspace could be built for about $7,000 in materials. With the outside walls built in the 16 inch solid bearing wall method and some 12 inch wide adobe parti-tion walls, about 4,000 adobes would be needed.

Scrutinize your local equipment rental businesses to see what they have.

It is not necessary to have electric power on the building site. All of our digging, sawing and drilling were done by hand. Several times I had to drill 12 inch holes in the concrete foundation for water pipes, and this was done with a star bit and a 2½ pound hammer.

Tiling a shower or a sink counter is not difficult. There are plastic adhesives that permit tiles to be glued directly onto a plywood backing. We used a mottled green Japanese ceramic tile with wavey edges and grouted the joints with gray mortar. Instructions and the simple tools needed can be obtained where one buys the tile and the adhesive.

Latex base paints are recommended if adobe walls are to be painted. Oil base paints will not do as the oil penetrates the bricks and bonds

The sixty-foot long porch, still incomplete. Note casement windows nearly flush with the wall, lintels above each.

with the asphalt. If the natural color is wanted, but something is needed to keep the adobes from shedding dust when touched then used a clear water seal such as Thompson's.

We were able to operate on a pay-as-you-go basis with regard to financing. If you wish to test the reaction of the upholders of the establishment when confronted with the true initiative and pioneer spirit that they claim to admire and nourish, then just try talking with your local lending institution officials; you'll find out that they mean the pioneers who are listed in Dun & Bradstreet. It is gratifying to be able to do without them.

If you are planning to buy an unimproved lot in the country, it is recommended that a thorough investigation be made concerning such items as those listed below. Your smiling real estate salesman may neglect to furnish accurate information.

1. Soil percolation and septic tank system sites. Many counties require proof of good soil percolation for disposal of septic tank effluent before they will issue a building permit. Usually, a lot must be at least an acre in size to allow for a home site, a well, and a septic tank leach field.

2. Cost of drilling a well, the probability of finding water, and the quality of that water.

3. Cost of bringing in electricity.

4. Access to the lot.

5. Boundaries. The corner posts shown to you may not be accurately located if a survey has not been made. The title insurance that I have seen (mine) does not insure against such mishaps.

6. Zoning and community development masterplans.

It is best to reckon on doing at least 95% of the work yourself because there is such a great amount of it that occasional volunteering by friends and relatives doesn't whittle off very much, no matter how much it is appreciated. Besides some general labor, as you go along you can expect to receive some helpful advice (a hod carrier taught me how to set string guides), some skilled work (a retired window glazer put all the glass in my window frames), and various gifts and loans of tools and materials. It all helps, and at least it is nice to have company.

We have been living in our adobe home for 6 months now and there are still portions of it that are not yet finished. In building an adobe, it seems natural for the builder to want to make everything himself. To cover the concrete slab floors, I plan to make some 1,400 big red tiles of the type used in the early California missions. This will take some experimenting, but at least I know of a good source of fire clay nearby. Doors in the house will be sturdy fabrications of planks and old wrough-iron square nails. The square nails I picked up on the sites of long since rotted-away flumes in the Sierra Nevada, which the "49ers" built to carry water to their diggings in the Mother Lode gold belt. In trying to copy the old technique of driving the nails through the wood and then bending or clinching the protruding end, I found that they will break off instead of bending if the end is not heated red hot to make it less brittle.

It is a fine thing to live in a house that has an inspiring character. Decorative items for such a structure have to have a corresponding basic integrity. From mines and prospects in the U. S. and Mexico where I have worked there are rich ore samples, curiously formed rocks, and old tools, such as a wooden gold pan. The Mayo and the Tarahumara Indians in northwestern Mexico have supplied wool blankets, baskets, weaving implements, and a smoke-darkened rawhide drum. From the Pre-Spanish Indian cultures of Sinaloa, and particularly the Culiacan region, there are stone axheads, clay pipes, ornaments of worked sea-shell, and clay spindle whorls with incised designs. Ranchos in the Sierra Madre are represented by rawhide riatas, large red ollas, and handkerchiefs embroidered by young senoritas with romantic symbols and declarations. One of our most unusual items is a 4 inch long ripple-flaked obsidian knife blade lost long ago by an Indian hunter and found by me when I was excavating dirt to make the adobes.

Making and building with the adobe brick entails involvement with many of man's oldest and most fundamental needs, skills, attitudes and experiences. We have found it all to have been well worth the time and effort spent.

The main room, with fireplace and floor still incomplete.

APPENDICES

Nearly 30 years ago I lived for a few months in one of four adobe duplex units in the desert at Thermal, California. At the time the extraordinary feeling of comfort and well-being I experienced there seemed to be due to their good construction. Over the years, I came to realize that there was a more subtle and complex explanation which included the tender loving care supplied by the young couple who were builder-owner-tenant-caretakers, and some other ingredient adobe seems to radiate just by being adobe.

Gene Boudreau and I became good friends as soon as we met about twelve years ago, and he worked for me a short time before his first trip to Mexico, where he met his wife, Sylvia. I saw them for the first time in several years recently, after they had raised the walls on this house, and I helped them celebrate the event.

I have thought about building my own from time to time, and have kept a file of information about adobe construction, but I was never able to find a book which told me what I needed to know. The urge is getting stronger now, and with Gene's book in my library, I expect to create the opportunity to actually start as soon as possible. If you live close enough to make use of his personal services, as I will, I would certainly recommend it.

I believe Gene has treated the engineering and building code aspects very well in this book, but the requirements will vary over a wide range for readers in different areas. Less conservative construction has been built by laymen long ago which has lasted many years. If one follows the principles outlined in the first paragraph of the section on "Loose Ends", I am sure any problems in this area will be adequately resolved. Now, get started!

R. Wm. Rollins
Registered Civil Engineer 8855, California
August 1971.

UNIFORM BUILDING CODE REQUIREMENTS FOR ADOBE BRICKS

Many counties base their building codes on the Uniform Building Code, in which are included certain standards set for "unburned clay brick", meaning adobe bricks, and their use. Anyone planning to make adobes should consult with his local county building permit office to see if they require anything in the way of standards beyond those set by the Uniform Building Code. If your county has not adopted the Uniform Building Code and has no other standards then it is still a good practice to conform with the U.B.C. Copies can be found in libraries and book stores.

The following is quoted from Uniform Building Code Standard No. 24-15, in the 1970 edition of the Uniform Building Code Standards.

"Sec. 24.1501. This Standard covers unburned clay masonry units made from a suitable mixture of soil, clay, and stabilizing agent, and intended for use in brick masonry.

"Sec. 24.1502. (a) Soil. The soil used shall contain not less than 25% and not more than 45% of material passing a No. 200 mesh sieve. The soil shall contain sufficient clay to bind the particles together, but shall not contain more than 0.2% of water soluble salts.

(b) Stabilizer. The stabilizing agent shall be emulsified asphalt. The stabilizing agent shall be uniformly mixed with the soil in amounts sufficient to provide the required resistance to absorption.

"Sec. 24.1503. At the time of delivery to the site of the work the units shall conform to the physical requirements prescribed in Table No. 24-1, A.

"Sec. 24.1504. No units shall contain more than three shrinkage cracks, and no shrinkage crack shall exceed 3 inches in length or ¼ inch in width.

"Sec. 24.1505. These methods cover procedures for the sampling and testing of unburned clay masonry units for compressive strength, modulus of rupture, absorption, and moisture content.

"Sec. 24.1506. For each of the tests prescribed in this Standard, five sample units shall be selected at random from each lot of 5,000 units or fraction thereof.

"Sec. 24.1507. Each specimen shall be marked so that it may be identified at any time. Markings shall cover not more than 5% of the superficial area of the specimen.

"Sec. 24.1508. Compressive strength tests shall be conducted in accordance with U.B.C. Standard No. 24-26.

"Sec. 24.1509. Five full-size specimens shall be tested for modulus of rupture according to the following procedure: . . . . . .

"Sec. 24.1510. A 4-inch cube cut from a sample unit shall be tested for absorption according to the following procedure:

1. Dry specimen to a constant weight in a ventilated oven at 212°F-239°F.

2. Place specimen on a constantly water-saturated porous surface for seven days. Weigh specimen.

3. Calculate absorption as a percentage of the initial dry weight.

"Sec. 24.1511. Five representative specimens shall be tested for moisture content according to the following procedure:

1. Obtain the weight of each specimen immediately upon receiving.

2. Dry all specimens to constant weight in a ventilated oven at 212°F.-239°F. and obtain dry weight.

3. Calculate absorption as a percentage of the initial dry weight."

I am not quoting the procedures for the tests for compressive strength and modulus of rupture as they require special equipment; but commercial testing laboratories can do them, though you can't.

Table No. 24-1-A states that the minimum compressive strength shall average 300 pounds per square inch for 5 tests, but no individual shall test less than 250. The average of 5 tests for modulus of rupture shall be a minimum of 50 pounds per square inch, but no individual shall test less than 35. Maximum water absorption in pounds per cubic foot, based on % of dry weight, shall not be more than 2.5%. Maximum moisture content, based on % of dry weight, shall not be more than 4.0%.

FIREPLACE & CHIMNEY DETAILS
Sonoma County Building Department

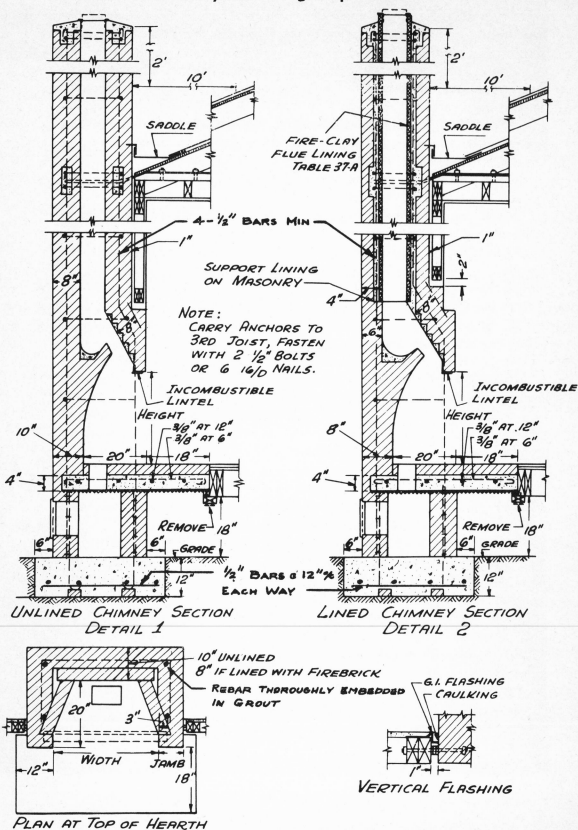

Detail 1 (left):

SADDLE

2'

10'

4 - ½" BARS MIN

1"

8"

8"

SUPPORT LINING ON MASONRY

NOTE:
CARRY ANCHORS TO 3RD JOIST, FASTEN WITH 2 ½" BOLTS OR 6 16/D NAILS.

INCOMBUSTIBLE LINTEL

HEIGHT

3/8" AT 12"
3/8" AT 6"

10"
20"
18"
4"

REMOVE 18"
6"
6"
GRADE
12"

½" BARS @ 12"% EACH WAY

UNLINED CHIMNEY SECTION
DETAIL 1

Detail 2 (right):

FIRE-CLAY FLUE LINING TABLE 37-A

SADDLE

2'

10'

1"

2"

4"
8"
6"

INCOMBUSTIBLE LINTEL

HEIGHT

3/8" AT 12"
3/8" AT 6"

8"
20"
18"
4"

REMOVE 18"
6"
6"
GRADE
12"

LINED CHIMNEY SECTION
DETAIL 2

Bottom left:

10" UNLINED
8" IF LINED WITH FIREBRICK
REBAR THOROUGHLY EMBEDDED IN GROUT

20"
3"

12"
WIDTH
JAMB
18"

PLAN AT TOP OF HEARTH

Bottom right:

G.I. FLASHING
CAULKING

1"

VERTICAL FLASHING

Fireplace going up, but not yet cut through the roof. The rebars are bent into place as you go. Note firebrick around the hearth beneath the adobes. Hearth will be faced with homemade ceramic brick.

ENGINEERING CALCULATIONS

General Design Criteria

    1. Adobe   Construction

    2. Adobe   blocks to conform   to   section   2405
        1964   U.B.C.   Unburned   Clay Masonry

    3. Construction   to   conform   to   Chapter   24 - Masonry   1964 U.B.C.

Plan

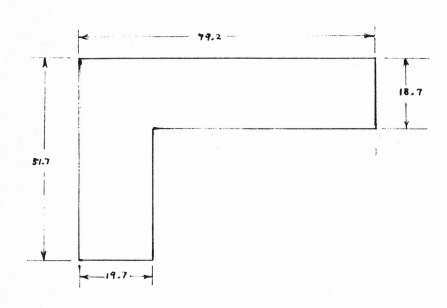

Roof

Kitchen — office - Bedroom - Bath   shall   be   framed   according to
Chapter   25   U.B.C.   1964   edition

Roof   Rafters   and   ceiling   joists   shall   be   construction grade
D.F.   f 1500   or   better.

D.L.	shakes -	4
	2" T&G -	4
	Plywood -	1
	Misc -	1
		10
L.L.		20
		30 #/ϕ

4×6   Rafters   @   4' o.c.   span =   8'

    load / ft   =   (4.37) (30) =   131 #/ft

From D.F. Use Book 4×6 Good for $285 \#/ft > 131 \therefore OK$

<u>Ridge Beam</u> $4'' \times 8''$

$$(131)(8) = 1048 \ \#/ft \qquad \downarrow \qquad Span \times 8'$$

$$M = \frac{PL}{4} = \frac{(1048)(8)}{4} \qquad 2096 \ '\#$$

$$S = \frac{(2096)(12)}{33.98} = 740 \ psi < 1500 \qquad OK$$

Total load @ tie $= (8)(8)(30) = 1920 \#$

Tie joists to take load directly from roof

$6'' \times 8''$ Beam   Span $\approx 19'$ $M = \frac{(1920)(19)}{4} = 9120 \ '\#$

$$S = \frac{(9120)(12)}{(51.56)(1.25)} = 1695 > 1500 \ psi$$

Use truss method with tie every $8'$

Bolt connection @ base must develop $2890 \#$

$\sphericalangle = 18°$ Try $5/8'' \ \phi$ bolts

allowable load /bolt $= 940 \#$

$$\frac{2890}{(940)(1.25)} = 2.45 \qquad say \ \underline{\underline{3}} \ bolts \quad 5/8'' \ \phi$$

3- $5/8'' \ \phi$ bolts with $3/8''$ metal washers

3'' Min

$1\frac{1}{2}''$ Min

4×6

4×6 or 6×8 @ owner's option

see sheet #3 for $\sphericalangle$ @ base of 4×6 Typical at all connections

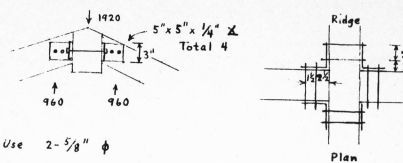

Use   2 - $\frac{5}{8}$" ϕ

Wall

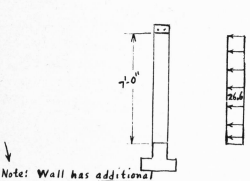

Note: Wall has additional strength due to reinforcing.

Assume Adobe bricks @   100 $^\#/ft^3$

Wind load =   20 $^\#/ft^2$

Seismic = $V = ZKCW$
$$= (1)(1)(.2)(133)$$
$$= 26.6 \; ^\#/\phi \quad \longleftarrow \text{use this}$$

Maximum H of adobe = 7'

$$M = \frac{We^2}{8} = \frac{(26.6)(7)^2}{8} = 163' \; ^\#/ft$$

$$f \; (T \pm C) = \frac{MC}{I} = \frac{(163)(12)(8)}{\frac{(12)(16)^3}{12}} = 3.82 \; p.s.i.$$

allowable = 4 psi without special inspection

load @ $\mathcal{R}$ $\frac{(26.6)(8.17)}{2}$ =   108.8   = 109 $^\#/ft$

Bond beam which is   8" x 12" with 4 - $\frac{1}{2}$" ϕ is OK
by inspection   to span   horizontally 4'

load / 4x6 rafter =   (109)(4) $\approx$ 436 $^\#$

Use   2 - $\frac{5}{8}$" ϕ

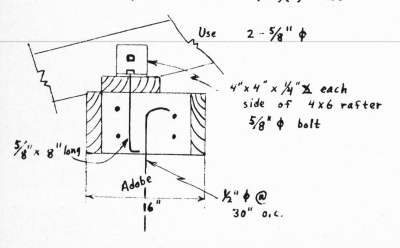

4" x 4" x $\frac{1}{4}$" $\angle$ each
side of 4x6 rafter
$\frac{5}{8}$" ϕ bolt

$\frac{5}{8}$" x 8" long

Adobe

16"

$\frac{1}{2}$" ϕ @
30" o.c.

(2)(200)(1.33) = 533 $^\#$
for adobe stress however
bolts are imbedded
8" in concrete
allowable load for
concrete (2)(1000)(1.33)
$\approx$ 2660 $^\#$ OK

Check Lintels

Wood may <u>not</u> support concrete ∴ Use concrete header

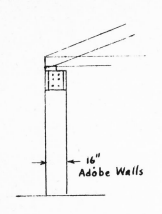

16"
Adobe Walls

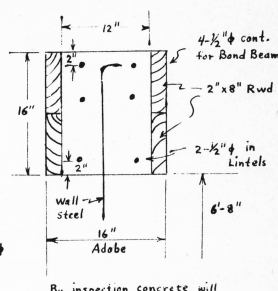

12"

2"

16"

2"

4-½"φ cont.
for Bond Beam

2"x8" Rwd

2-½"φ in
Lintels

Wall
steel

16"
Adobe

6'-8"

Beam over all openings will be

12" x 16" Concrete with 6-½"φ
top   Bottom

Maximum opening is <u>4'-0"</u>

By inspection concrete will
be adequate.

Lateral Loads

Wind = 20 #/φ   top loading = (7)(20) = 140 #/ft

Seismic = Walls (2)(133)(4) = 1065
⊥ to long Dim Roof (30.5)(10) = $\underline{305}$
                              1370 #/ft   (0.1) = 137 #/ft

∴ Use Wind as control (Living & Dining Room)

⊥ to long Dim = Walls   = 1065
(Living Room) Ceiling (17)(10)   = 170
               Roof (25.67)(10) = $\underline{257}$
                              1492 #/ft (0.1) = 149 #/ft

⊥ to short Dim
(Bedroom)   Walls   1065
            Partitions (2)(4)(100) 800
               "   (2)(4)(12)   96
            Ceiling (49)(10)   490
            Roof (57.7)(10) $\underline{577}$
                              3028 #/ft (0.1) = 303 #/ft

Seismic (cont.)

⊥ to short Dim
   (Living Rm)

Walls	1065
Partitions	800
"	96
Ceiling (45)(10)	450
Roof (85)(10)	850
	3261 #/ft (0.1) = 326 #/ft

For Analysis assume wings independent

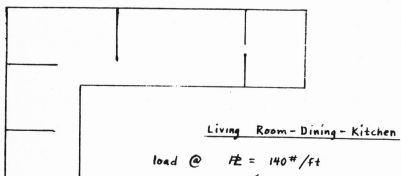

Living Room - Dining - Kitchen

load @ F_2 = 140 #/ft

Total V = (59.5) (140) = 8330 #

Assume taken by end wall & wall between Living Rm & office (adobe shear wall with bond beam)

Load /wall = 4165 #/wall

shear = $\frac{4165}{15.7}$ = 266 #/ft

$v = \frac{266}{(12)(16)} = 1.38$ psi ← adobe shear stress

Allowable = 4 psi OK

Partition wall
(12" "t") $v = \frac{266}{(12)(12)} = 1.85$ psi OK

⊥ to short Dimension load @ F_2 = 326 #/ft

Total V = (326) (18.67) = 6080 #

or 3040 #/wall

or $\frac{3040}{44}$ = 69 #/ft OK by inspection

Bedroom

OK by inspection

Loads ⊥ to long dimension will be resisted by plywood roof with loads transfered to end walls

Loads ⊥ to end walls will take load in top bond beam in bending

@ Kitchen

$$load = (7)(20) = 140 \ \#/ft \ @ \ R$$

$$M = \frac{(190)(16)^2}{8} = 4480 \ '\#$$

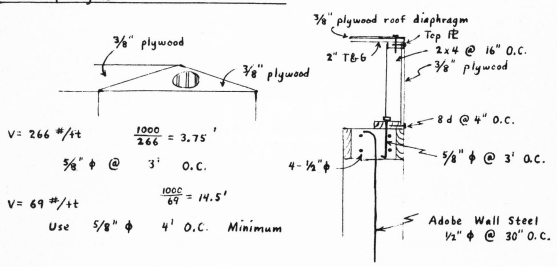

$$M_R = (0.067)(236) = 15.8 \ \ IK$$

$$or \ 15,800 \ '\# \ > \ 4480$$

∴ OK

$$A_{s_{reqd.}} = \frac{M}{ad}$$

$$= \frac{4.48}{(1.44)(10)} = .312 \ \#$$

$$2 - \tfrac{1}{2}" \ \phi = 0.4 \ \ OK$$

<u>Roof Diaphragm</u>

Need   3/8" plywood over   T & G   or   Rafters

with   8d nails @   4" O.C.   all panel edges
8d   "   "   12" O.C.   in field
allowable shear resistance   =   298 #/ft

<u>End walls and interior walls which act as
shear diaphragms</u>

V = 266 #/ft $\frac{1000}{266} = 3.75 '$

5/8" φ @ 3' O.C.

V = 69 #/ft $\frac{1000}{69} = 14.5'$

Use   5/8" φ   4' O.C. Minimum

3/8" plywood
3/8" plywood

3/8" plywood roof diaphragm
Top R
2" T&G
2 x 4 @ 16" O.C.
3/8" plywood
8d @ 4" O.C.
4 - 1/2" φ
5/8" φ @ 3' O.C.
Adobe Wall Steel
1/2" φ @ 30" O.C.

Foundations

Roof load	–	(30)(13)	=	390 #
Wall		(133)(8)	=	1060 #
Porch	≈	(4)(30)		120
Foundation Wall			=	300
Ftg			=	532
				2402 #/ft

Width of ftg = 32" (2.67') @ 1000 #/ϕ = $\underline{2670}$ #   O.K.

12 Sept. '67

Minimum area of total reinforcing shall be not less than
(0.002) (gross × sec area)
Not more than 2/3 of which may be in either direction

(16" × 12")(.002) =   .384   #/ft of wall

Try #5 @ 30" O.C = $\dfrac{0.31}{2.5}$ =   .124   #/ft of wall vert.

($\frac{1}{3}$).384 = .128   ≈   .124   OK

Need   0.260   #/ft   Horizontal

Try #5 @ 16" O.C. $\dfrac{0.21}{1.33}$ = .233 #/ft

Try #5 @ 24" OC $\dfrac{0.31}{2}$ = 0.155 #/ft

Total = 0.388 #/ft

Or Try #4 @ 12" O.C.   O.K.

PERCOLATION TEST PROCEDURE*

1. *Number and location of tests.*

A. Single Lots—Three or more tests shall be made in separate test holes spaced uniformly over each proposed absorption-field site.

B. Subdivision requirements—A minimum of 1 test hole per acre for subdivision, more may be required.

2. *Type of test hole.* Dig or bore a hole, with horizontal dimensions of from 6 to 12 inches and with vertical sides, to the depth of the proposed absorption trench, usually 36 inches.

3. *Preparation of test hole.* Remove all loose material from the hole. Add two inches of coarse sand or fine gravel to protect the bottom from scouring and sediment. Insert cylindrical wire screen or perforated bituminous fiber pipe to prevent sloughing. If perforated pipe is used, fill the space surrounding the pipe with clean gravel.

4. Prior to conducting the test, fill the hole completely with clear water. In most soils it is necessary to refill the hole by supplying a surplus reservoir of water. Following adequate presoaking the test should give comparable results in the same soil, whether made in a dry or in a wet season.

Saturation and swelling of the soil. It is important to distinguish between saturation and swelling. Saturation means that the v o i d spaces between soil particles are full of water. This can be accomplished in a short period of time. Swelling is caused by intrusion of water into the individual soil particle. This is a slow process, especially in clay-type soil, and is the reason for requiring a prolonged soaking period.

5. *Percolation-rate measurement.* Percolation-rate measurements shall be made on the day following the procedure described under item 4, above.

A. If water remains in the test hole after the overnight soaking period, adjust the depth to approximately 12 inches over the gravel or as specified by the Health Officer. From a fixed reference point, measure the drop in water level over a six-hour period. The last readings are used to calculate the stabilized percolation rate.

B. If no water remains in the hole after the overnight soaking period, add clear water to bring the depth of water in the hole to approximately 12 inches over the gravel or as specified by the Health Officer. From a fixed reference point, measure the drop in water level at 60 minute intervals for 6 hours. If hole goes dry, refill to 12 inches over the gravel and resume testing. The last readings are used to calculate the stabilized percolation rate. The reading during prior periods provides information for possible modification of the procedure to suit local circumstances.

C. In soils in which the bottom 12 inches seeps away in less than 30 minutes, after the overnight soaking period, the time interval between measurements shall be taken as 10 minutes and the test run for 2 hours or repeated twice. The last readings are used to calculate the percolation rate.

6A. *Absorption-rate requirements* for private residences. (Provides for Garbage-Grinder and Automatic-Sequence Washing Machines.)

Percolation rate (Time required for water to fall 1 inch, in minutes)	Required absorption area, in square feet per bedroom[1] standard trench[2] and seepage pits[3]	Percolation rate (Time required for water to fall 1 inch, in minutes)	Required absorption area, in square feet per bedroom[1] standard trench[2] and seepage pits[3]
1 or less	70	10	165
2	85	15	190
3	100	30[4]	250
4	115	45[4]	300
5	125	60[4] [5]	330

6B. *Percolation Test Results.* Areas in which the ground water table is within 24 inches of the ground surface are not considered suitable for subsurface sewage disposal.

7. The testing procedures for soil percolation must be observed as described herein to insure valid results. Percolation test data must be submitted upon the forms provided.

8. Official percolation tests require the services of a registered civil engineer or licensed land surveyor.

9. This department must be notified at least 48 hours in advance of any soil percolation testing.

10. Submit on the page provided for that purpose a sketch of the area tested, showing approximate location of test holes with respect to property lines.

*Basically developed at the Robert A. Taft Sanitary Engineering Center and used by the Sonoma County Department of Health Services.

[1]In every case, sufficient area should be provided for at least two bedrooms.
[2]Absorption area for standard trenches is figured as trench-bottom area.
[3]Absorption area for seepage pits is figured as effective side-wall area beneath the inlet.
[4]Unsuitable for seepage pits if over 30.
[5]Unsuitable for leaching systems if over 60.

DISPOSAL FIELD
Typical Examples

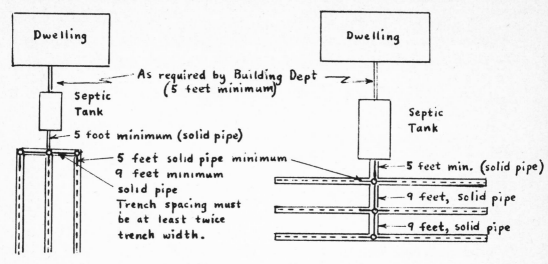

Dwelling

Septic Tank

As required by Building Dept (5 feet minimum)

5 foot minimum (solid pipe)

5 feet solid pipe minimum
9 feet minimum
solid pipe
Trench spacing must
be at least twice
trench width.

Dwelling

Septic Tank

5 feet min. (solid pipe)

9 feet, solid pipe

9 feet, solid pipe

Note: all trench bottoms must be level
Dash line indicates perforated pipe

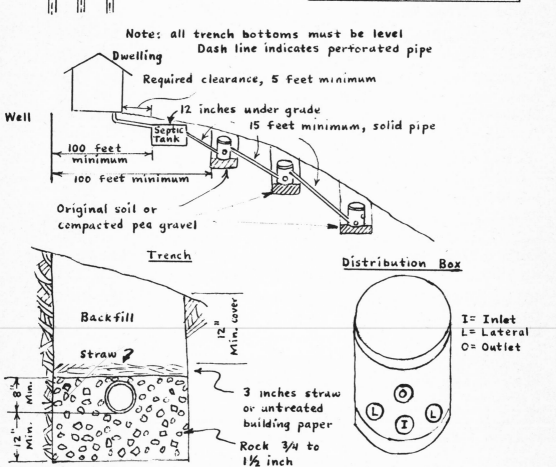

Dwelling

Required clearance, 5 feet minimum

12 inches under grade

15 feet minimum, solid pipe

Septic Tank

Well

100 feet minimum

100 feet minimum

Original soil or
compacted pea gravel

Trench

Backfill

Straw

12" Min. cover

8" Min.

12" Min.

3 inches straw
or untreated
building paper

Rock 3/4 to
1½ inch

Distribution Box

I = Inlet
L = Lateral
O = Outlet

BIBLIOGRAPHY 87

1. *How to Plan and Build Your Fireplace*, Lane Books, Menlo Park, $1.95

2. *Wiring Handbook*, Sears & Roebuck, Catalog No. 34A5428, $0.50.

3. *How to Design and Install Plumbing*, Sears & Roebuck, Catalog No. 3A1309, $5.49.

4. *Manual of Septic Tank Practice*, U.S. Department of Health, Education, and Welfare, Public Health Service Publication No. 526, $0.35. Order from Superintendent of Documents, U.S. Government Printing Office, Washington, D.C. 20201.

5. *Wiring Simplified*, by H. P. Richter, Park Publishing, Inc., P.O. Box 5527 (Lake St. Sta.), Minneapolis, Minn. 55408. $0.75. This is a good book and one that is up to Code.

6. *Practical House Carpentry*, by J. Douglas Wilson, McGraw-Hill Book Company, Inc. 1957.

7. *Build Your Own Adobe*, by Paul and Doris Aller, Stanford University Press, Stanford University, California. Out of print, so try your library. This book is interesting reading, but many of the building practices described are not allowed by the Uniform Building Code.

8. *The Principals of Chemical Weathering*, by Keller, Lucas Brothers Publishers, Columbia, Missouri. This book explains how different clay minerals form in different environments.

9. *Soils Suitable for Septic Tank Filter Fields*, by William H. Bender, U.S. Dept. of Agriculture, Agriculture Information Bulletin No. 243. Order from the Superintendent of Documents, U.S. Government Printing Office, Washington 25, D.C. Price 15c.

10. *Uniform Building Code*, 1970 Edition, Vol. I, International Conference of Building Officials, 50 South Los Robles, Pasadena, Calif. 91101.

11. *Uniform Plumbing Code,* 1970 Edition. International Association of Plumbing and Mechanical Officials, 5032 Alhambra Ave., Los Angeles, California 90032.

12. *National Electrical Code* (most recent available) National Fire Prevention Association, 60 Batterymarch St., Boston, Mass. 02110.

13. *The Forgotten Art of Building a Good Fireplace*, by Vrest Orten, Yankee, Inc., Dublin, New Hampshire, 03444. Price $2. I highly recommend this book as a superior guide to building a smokeless fireplace with high heat emission.

14. *Buying Country Land*, by Eugene H. Boudreau, The Macmillan Company, 866 Third Avenue, New York, New York 10022. Price $1.25 paper and $3.95 hardcover. A guide to checking on the suitability of underdeveloped country land for a homesite. Highly recommended.

15. *Minimum Standards for a Private Water Well in Nebraska*, 1972. Order from the Nebraska Department of Health, Lincoln, Nebraska. No charge. Has good information on ground water and wells.

NOTE: The UBC, the UPC and the NEC (as well as local codes) are available from the Reference Desk of your library.

We would enjoy having your comments on MAKING THE ADOBE BRICK. Please address them to the author at:

Eugene H. Boudreau
2600 Pleasant Hill Road
Sebastopol, California 95472

People wanting a reply are requested to enclose a stamped, self-addressed envelope.

COLOPHON

MAKING THE ADOBE BRICK is set in 10 point GOUDY enlarged 120%. Headings are set in 18 pt. Spartan Medium.

The paper stock is 60 lb. Alpine Opaque Vellum.

MAKING THE ADOBE BRICK was printed offset and perfect bound in 7 by 10½ inch format.

Special thanks to Hank Goodman, Paul de Fremery and Suzy Weakley, 547 Howard St., San Francisco, without whose production expertise this book couldn't have been.

Please address orders to Random House, Westminster, Md.